illustrated by
Mitch Vane

First Published in Great Britain by
RISING STARS UK LTD 2006
22 Grafton Street, London, W1S 4EX

For more information visit our website at:
www.risingstars-uk.com

British Library Cataloguing in Publication Data
A CIP record for this book is available from the British Library.

ISBN: 978-1-84680-052-8

First published in 2006 by
MACMILLAN EDUCATION AUSTRALIA PTY LTD
627 Chapel Street, South Yarra 3141

Visit our website at www.macmillan.com.au or
go directly to www.macmillanlibrary.com.au

Associated companies and representatives throughout the world.

Series created by Felice Arena and Phil Kettle
Project management by Limelight Press Pty Ltd
Cover and text design by Lore Foye
Illustrations by Mitch Vane

Printed in China

UK Editorial by Westcote Computing Editorial Services

Essex County
Council Libraries

Contents

Matt   *Nick*

CHAPTER 1

Pocket Money

It's Saturday morning and best friends Nick and Matt are talking about trying to earn some extra pocket money.

Matt "So, how are we going to earn some extra money?"

Nick "Maybe we could put a sign up on the front gate asking for work."

Matt "Even better—maybe we can just put a box on the pavement asking for donations."

Nick "Somehow I don't think that's going to work."

Matt "Yes, I think you're right."

Nick "We've got to try and find something that we can do together."

Matt "Something that's fun and makes heaps of money."

Nick "What about a paper round?"

Matt "Good idea."

Nick "But we can't do that together."

Matt "We could if we used the tandem bike that my parents have got in the garage."

Nick "How come they've got a tandem bike?"

Matt "Dad says Mum couldn't keep up with him on bike rides, so he bought it to stop her getting lost."

Nick "Well, I suppose she was a girl a long time ago, and girls aren't as fast as boys."

Matt "That's right, boys rule when it comes to speed."

Nick "So let's go and ask for a job at the paper shop."

Matt and Nick head down to the paper shop.

CHAPTER TWO

How Cool!

There's a sign in the window of the paper shop that says "Paper boy Wanted. Apply Inside".

Nick (pointing) "How cool is this? Looks like they're expecting us."
Nick "I think that job has got to be ours."

The paper shop owner tells them
that the paper round is only for one.
But when the boys tell him about the
tandem bike, he agrees to give them
a trial.

Matt "Let's go home and get the
bike ready for our first paper round
tomorrow."

Nick "I know that I'll be the best
steerer ever."

Matt "How come you get to steer?"

Nick "Because last time I saw you ride your bike, you rode into a fence."

Matt "Yes, but that's only because I was racing you, and I was going far too fast."

Nick "OK, then I think that we should take it in turns."

Matt "That's cool. Whoever sits on the
back gets to throw the newspapers.
We'll be so fast that the paper shop
man will probably pay us more money."

Nick "We might even be able to do
more than one paper round!"

Matt "Race you back home!"

The boys race each other back to
Matt's house to try to find the
tandem bike.

CHAPTER 3

Red Bikes Go the Fastest

The boys are standing in the garage
looking at the bike.

Matt "Well, I know one thing …"
Nick "Yes, we can't have a green
bike and expect to go fast."
Matt "Red bikes go the fastest."

Nick "Just like red cars, they go
faster than any other cars."

The boys hunt around in the
garage. Eventually they find a tin
of bright red paint. Soon the bike
is bright red, and so is most of the
garage floor.

Matt (pointing at the bike) "Wow, this
looks cool now."

Nick (looking worried) "What about the paint on the floor?"

Matt "I'll tell Dad that the tin of paint fell off the shelf and landed on the floor."

Nick "What? And you'll tell him that it just happened to fall on the bike first and cover it?"

Matt "Well, I think I'll tell him after we've done the paper round, when we show him all the money that we've made."

Nick "Cool, then he won't mind that we've painted his bike."

Matt and Nick find an old bag. When the paint is dry, they hang the bag over the back handlebars of the bike.

Matt "This has to be the best paper round bike ever."

Nick "Yes, we're really going to fly on this."

Matt "I can't wait until we start tomorrow."

CHAPTER 4

Ready, Steady, Go!

Next morning at five o'clock, Nick and Matt meet outside the paper shop.

Nick "I can't believe that we're up this early! It's still dark. Birds aren't even awake yet!"

Matt "Yes, no wonder the paper
    shop owner was looking for
    someone to do a paper round."

Just then Mr. Jones, the paper
shop owner appears at the door of
the paper shop. He tells them it's
time to wake up and get going.

Nick "I'm not sure that this is such
    a good idea."

Matt "Yes, I think I've just realised how much I love my bed. But I'm sure I'm going to love all the money that we make just as much."

Nick "Me too!"

Soon the boys have the bike loaded with papers and are ready to go. Mr. Jones tells them to take their time and do a good job.

Matt (looking at his watch) "Time for blast-off."

Nick "It's not a rocket."

Matt "Well, with me on the back throwing *and* pedalling we'll be travelling at the same speed as a rocket."

The boys head off. Nick has the
paper delivery route attached to his
handlebars.

Nick "I'll shout when you have to
throw."

Matt "This'll be just like throwing a
basketball."

Nick "First house coming up."

Matt picks a paper out of the bag.

Nick "Are you ready? Right ... throw now!"

Matt throws the paper. It lands in the front garden of the house.

Nick "You threw the paper into the house on the wrong side of the road."

Matt "You said 'right'."

Nick "Yes, I meant right to throw, not throw to the right. I meant the house on the left."

Matt "Well, we'll have to stop and put the paper in the right garden."

Nick "If we stop we'll never break the speed record for a paper round."

Matt "So what's the record?"

Nick "No idea."

Matt "But whatever it is, we want to break it."

Nick "That's right, the man in the house only has to walk across the road and he'll find his paper."

The boys keep pedalling.

Nick "Next house coming up. It's on the left this time."

Matt "Right!"

Nick "No, the house on the left."

Matt "OK ... OK ..."

Nick "Throw!"

Matt throws the paper. A crashing sound follows.

Nick "Sounds like something just broke."

Matt "I didn't hear anything."

Nick "Let's keep going ... faster! Faster!"

Matt "Look there's a man in his pyjamas. He must be waiting for his paper."

Nick "He must really like his paper!"

Matt "I'll throw it right at his feet."

Nick "Well, just make sure you don't land it in the puddle in front of him."

Matt "That's a three-pointer!"

Splash!

Nick "No, that's a paper in a puddle of water … and the water's all over the man in pyjamas."

CHAPTER 5

Trouble Ahead

Matt and Nick ride away as fast as they can.

Matt "Did you hear what the man said when we went past?"

Nick "I think that he said something about wanting to do something to us."

Matt "Maybe he wants to give us a tip."

The boys keep racing round the paper route, moving at the speed of light.

Matt "We've only got one more paper to deliver."

Nick "Next house on the left."

Matt "Right!"

Nick "Left and that will be right."

Matt "Good."

Matt throws the paper.

Clunk!

Nick "I think that paper landed on the roof."

Matt "That's OK. It'll roll off."

Nick "So, we're finished. Let's get back to the paper shop."

Matt "Yes, the paper shop owner will think that we're heroes."

Nick "Because we're so fast!"

The boys turn the corner and head towards the paper shop. Mr. Jones is standing in front of the shop with his arms crossed.

Matt (pointing) "Look, he's waiting to greet us."

Nick "He must be going to congratulate us."

Matt "Yes, I think that's what he's going to do."

Mr. Jones isn't smiling. He tells the boys that for the next three weeks they'll be working for nothing. As well as throwing papers into the wrong gardens, the boys broke a window and knocked the head off a garden gnome.

Nick "I knew it was too good to be true. This stinks!"

Matt "It's all your fault for trying to go so fast."

Nick "No, it's your fault for being so bad at throwing."

Matt "Well, tomorrow you get to throw."

Nick "I'll be better than you!"

Matt "Right!"

Nick "So, now we've got to go home and tell your father about all the paint on the garage floor."

Matt "And we've got to tell him that we messed up the paper round and we're not going to get paid for the next three weeks."

Nick "At least your Dad will be pleased that we fixed up his old bike."

Matt "Er, I think I forgot to mention
that my Dad told me I'm not
allowed to touch his bike."

Nick "Oh no, we're in really big
trouble."

Matt "I think perhaps we should go
to your house for a while."

Nick "Yes, you might want to stay
for the rest of the weekend."

BOYS RULE!
Paper Round Lingo

Nick

Matt

crash The sound you hear when the paper hits a window.

paper round Where you deliver the newspapers. Mostly it is to different houses in the same area or town.

paper shop owner The person who owns the paper shop—also the one who pays you when you do a paper round.

sunrises What you'll see a lot of if you do a paper round.

tandem bike A bike that's built so that two people can ride it at the same time. It has two sets of pedals and two sets of handlebars.

BOYS RULE!
Paper Round Must-dos

☞ Make sure that you deliver the paper to the right house.

☞ Pump up the tyres of your bike before you do your round.

☞ Don't ride through puddles. You might get the papers wet.

☞ Don't go around corners too fast when you're loaded with papers. You might end up in a heap on the road.

☞ Don't throw the paper near a window.

☞ If a dog barks at you, bark back. That might stop him from chasing you.

☞ Try not to land the paper on the roof. But if you do, yell out "Three points!"

☞ Don't throw the paper into any bushes. The owner of the house might not be able to find the paper, and you'll be in trouble.

☞ If you like sleeping in, make sure that you set your alarm so that you wake up in time to do your paper round.

☞ Save the money that you get paid, so that you can buy something that you really want.

BOYS RULE!
Paper Round
Instant Info

 Paper rounds are mostly done in the morning, and nearly always before the Sun comes up.

 Newspapers are usually rolled up to make them easier for the paper boy to deliver. Sometimes they're also rolled in plastic.

Paper boys who deliver the newspapers to the wrong houses don't usually keep their jobs for very long.

In the days before newspapers, people who wanted to know what the news was, had to go into the town square and listen to the Town Crier.

News comes from all over the world, from the North, East, West and South. So the word "news" is made up of the first letter of each point of the compass.

 Before paper boys did home deliveries, they used to stand on street corners selling papers. They would also call out the headlines of the day to try to get people to buy the paper.

BOYS RULE!
Think Tank

1 How many people ride a tandem bike at the same time?

2 How many wheels does a tandem bike have?

3 Who steers a tandem bike?

4 What is paper made from?

5 What do you call a person who writes stories for a newspaper?

6 What sport do you think would help you learn how to throw papers?

7 If you are a paper boy, what do you need to help you wake up in the morning?

8 What do you call a paper boy who rides through a puddle of water?

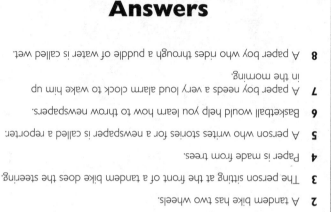

Answers

8 A paper boy who rides through a puddle of water is called wet.

7 A paper boy needs a very loud alarm clock to wake him up in the morning.

6 Basketball would help you learn how to throw newspapers.

5 A person who writes stories for a newspaper is called a reporter.

4 Paper is made from trees.

3 The person sitting at the front of a tandem bike does the steering.

2 A tandem bike has two wheels.

1 Two people ride a tandem bike at the same time.

How did you score?

- If you got all 8 answers correct, then you're ready to do your own paper round.

- If you got 6 answers correct, then you probably still need to do some training.

- If you got fewer than 4 answers correct, then maybe you should think of some other way to earn pocket money.

Felice →   ← Phil

Hi Guys!

We have heaps of fun reading and want you to, too. We both believe that being a good reader is really important and so cool.

Try out our suggestions to help you have fun as you read.

At school, why don't you use "Paper Round" as a play and you and your friends can be the actors. Set the scene for your play. Bring some newspapers to school to use as props and maybe even your bike, too! If you're doing the throwing, just be careful you don't break one of the school's windows.

So ... have you decided who is going to be Matt and who is going to be Nick? Now, with your friends, read and act out our story in front of the class.

We have a lot of fun when we go to schools and read our stories. After we finish the children all clap really loudly. When you've finished your play your classmates will do the same. Just remember to look out the window—there might be a talent scout from a television channel watching you!

Reading at home is really important and a lot of fun as well.

Take our books home and get someone in your family to read them with you. Maybe they can take on a part in the story.

Remember, reading is fun.

So, as the frog in the local pond would say, Read-it!

And remember, Boys Rule!

BOYS RULE!
When We Were Kids

Felice

Phil

Felice "Did you ever do a paper round?"

Phil "Yes, but only for one day."

Felice "How come you only did it for one day?"

Phil "I got fired!"

Felice "Why did you get fired?"

Phil "Well, as soon as I got a paper in my hand something happened."

Felice "Really? What was that?"

Phil "I thought I was playing basketball and the roofs of the houses were basketball rings."

Felice "That was silly!"

Phil "Yes, I know. I got fired, but I also scored a lot of three-pointers!"

42

What a Laugh!

Q What is black and white and red all over?

A A newspaper.

BOYS RULE!

Gone Fishing	The Tree House	Golf Legends	Camping Out	Bike Daredevils
Water Rats	Skateboard Dudes	Tennis Ace	Basketball Buddies	Secret Agent Heroes
Wet World	Rock Star	Pirate Attack	Olympic Champions	Race Car Dreamers
Hit the Beach	Rotten School Day	Halloween Gotcha!	Battle of the Games	On the Farm